Inglés sin Barreras

El Video-Maestro de Inglés Conversacional

8 La Salud

Cuaderno de ejercicios

Para información sobre
Inglés sin Barreras
en oferta especial de
Referido Preferido
1-800-305-6472
Dé el Código 03429

La Salud

Índice

No se olvide de estudiar las lecciones en el manual antes de hacer los ejercicios de este cuaderno.

Examen Inicial

Antes de comenzar el estudio de este volumen, dedique unos minutos a contestar a las 15 preguntas del examen siguiente. Llene el círculo correspondiente a la respuesta correcta.

1. *My shoulder* _____.
   - ○ a) has a backache
   - ○ b) is a pain
   - ○ c) pains
   - ○ d) aches
   - ○ e) ache

2. _____ *his elbow* _____?
   - ○ a) Why does, hurts
   - ○ b) Why, aches
   - ○ c) Do, aches
   - ○ d) Do, ache
   - ○ e) Does, hurt

3. *Do you* _____ *earache?*
   - ○ a) hurt some
   - ○ b) have an
   - ○ c) have
   - ○ d) have a
   - ○ e) hurt an

4. *What's the* _____?
   - ○ a) stomache
   - ○ b) hurt
   - ○ c) hurt
   - ○ d) matter
   - ○ e) wrong

5. *I have a __ throat and a ____.*
   - ○ a) hurt, temperature
   - ○ b) ache, temperature
   - ○ c) sore, fever
   - ○ d) sore, runny
   - ○ e) fever, sore

6. *The pharmacist's* _____ *was very helpful.*
   - ○ a) temperature
   - ○ b) cold
   - ○ c) prescribe
   - ○ d) symptom
   - ○ e) advice

7. *Those shoes hurt my feet.* _____ *wear them.*
   - ○ a) I shouldn't
   - ○ b) She should
   - ○ c) I can
   - ○ d) She can
   - ○ e) I am

8. *You are* _____ *a lot. You should see the doctor.*
   - ○ a) ache
   - ○ b) fever
   - ○ c) coughing
   - ○ d) runny nose
   - ○ e) sneeze

9. *Drink lots of___ rest and take two* _____.
   - ○ a) orange juice, pill
   - ○ b) coffee, medicines
   - ○ c) fluids, aspirin
   - ○ d) medicine, tablets
   - ○ e) water, capsule

10. *Listening to the message on an answering machine* _____ *usually difficult.*
    - ○ a) happened
    - ○ b) is
    - ○ c) shouldn't
    - ○ d) has
    - ○ e) happens

11. *To hear this* _____ *again, press the star key.*
    - ○ a) appointments
    - ○ b) reception
    - ○ c) speaking
    - ○ d) phone
    - ○ e) message

12. *This medicine __ cause drowsiness.*
    - ○ a) don't
    - ○ b) should
    - ○ c) wasn't
    - ○ d) isn't
    - ○ e) may

13. ___*does the prescription have?*
    - ○ a) When
    - ○ b) How much
    - ○ c) How many refills
    - ○ d) How many
    - ○ e) How possible

14. *Did the doctor __ you a prescription?*
    - ○ a) give
    - ○ b) mark
    - ○ c) make
    - ○ d) recommended
    - ○ e) tell

15. *2 tsp. 3 X day* _____
    - ○ a) Take three tablets daily.
    - ○ b) Take 2 teaspoons at 3:00 each day.
    - ○ c) Take two tablets twice a day.
    - ○ d) Take 2 tablespoons three times a day.
    - ○ e) Take 2 teaspoons three times a day.

Cuando haya estudiado todas las lecciones de este volumen, haga el mismo examen de nuevo. Lo encontrará al final de este cuaderno, en la página titulada "Examen Final".

Compare los resultados obtenidos en este examen con los del examen final. Así comprobará lo que ha aprendido y podrá medir su progreso.

Cuando haya terminado este examen, empiece a estudiar la Lección Uno.

Lección

1 Notas

Encontrará las respuestas en la página 12.

A. Resuelva el crucigrama.

Primero, complete las oraciones. Después, escriba las palabras que completan las oraciones en el cuadro siguiente, empezando por la casilla que lleva el número correspondiente.

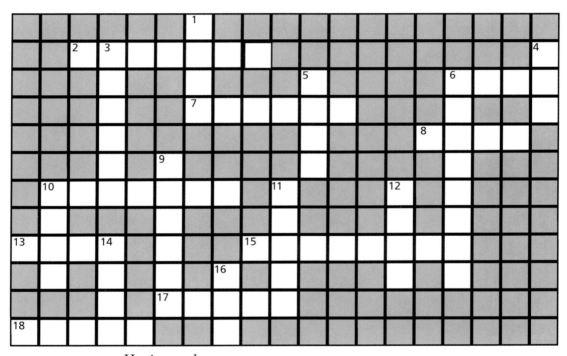

Horizontales

2.

6. My arm hurts.
   It's very _____.

7.

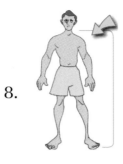

8.

10. He is Dr. Martin's _____.

13. She felt _____ so she went home.

 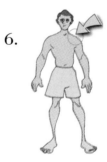 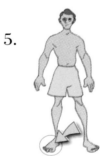

15. 17. 18.

Verticales

1. 3. He has a sore _____.

4. 5. 6.

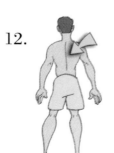

9. Take care of your _____.

10. She has a _____ in her arm.

11.  12.  14.  16.

B. Delante de cada oración, escriba la letra del dibujo correspondiente.

Ejemplo: ___*e*___ Her leg hurts.

1. _____ She has a backache.

2. _____ Their arms hurt.

3. _____ She has an earache.

4. _____ His head hurts.

5. _____ She has a stomachache.

6. _____ He has a pain in his neck.

7. _____ I think his toe hurts.

Clase

Encontrará las respuestas en la página 13.

C. Complete las oraciones relacionadas con los dibujos. En ciertos casos, hay más de una respuesta correcta.

Ejemplo: He has a pain in his ____*knee*____.

1.   His knee _____.

2.   His _____ hurts.

3.   He has a _____ shoulder.

4.   His _____ aches.

5.   Does his elbow _____?

6.   The man _____ a sore throat.

7.   His neck _____, too.

8.   _____ chest aches.

9.   He has a _____ in his chest.

D. Escriba las preguntas correspondientes a estas oraciones. Use las palabras entre paréntesis.

Ejemplo: He has a headache.

Does he have a headache?

1. Her stomach hurts.

   _____

2. Their shoulders ache.

   _____

3. She is sick.

   _____

4. The pain is in his knee.

   _____

5. My knee is sore.

   (you) _____

6. My wife has a stomachache.

   (you) _____

7. He hurt his arm yesterday.

   _____

8. I feel better today.

   (you) _____

Diálogo

Encontrará las respuestas en la página 14.

Elija la respuesta correcta.

1. Angel   How are you today?
   Mario   Not too good.
              a) I feel great.
              b) I have a headache.

2. Julio   a) What's the matter?
              b) I don't feel well.
   Kim   Oh. You look fine.

3. Jim   I have a pain in my chest.
   Kathy   a) Does it hurt?
              b) Is it a sharp pain?

4. Lee   My leg hurts.
   Joseph   a) Is it your knee or your ankle?
              b) Is it your wrist or your elbow?

5. Barbara   Do you have a stomachache?
   Sam   a) No, the pain is in my chest.
              b) Yes, the pain is in my chest.

6. Terry   a) My wife is sick.
              b) I am ill.
   Nurse   Where is her pain?

Encontrará las respuestas en la página 14.

Llene los espacios en blanco con las palabras indicadas a continuación.

hurts	~~backache~~	pain	matter	sharp
ache	earache	ankle	feel	sore

Ejemplo: She has a ___*backache*___.

1. My head _____.

2. She has an _____.

3. I have a _____ in my shoulder.

4. Is the pain in your knee or your _____?

5. Do you _____ OK?

6. It's a _____ pain.

7. My knees _____.

8. What's the _____?

9. Do you have a _____ throat?

Vocabulario

A.

The completed crossword puzzle:

- 1. H
- 2. STOMACH
- 3. T / THROAT
- 4. L / LEG
- 5. F / FOOT
- 6. SORE
- 7. DOCTOR
- 8. BODY
- 9. H
- 10. PATIENT / PAIN
- 11. CHEST
- 12. B / BACK
- 13. SICK / SKIN
- 14. K / KNEE
- 15. HEADACHE
- 16. E / EYES
- 17. HEART
- 18. BONES

Crossword grid letters:

Row 1: H
Row 2: S T O M A C H / L
Row 3: H N F S O R E
Row 4: R D O C T O R H G
Row 5: O O B O D Y
Row 6: A H T U
Row 7: P A T I E N T C B L
Row 8: A A H A D
Row 9: S I C K L H E A D A C H E
Row 10: N N T E S K R
Row 11: E H E A R T
Row 12: B O N E S R

B.

1. d
2. h
3. g
4. a
5. b
6. f
7. c

Clase

C.

1. hurts (*or* aches)
2. shoulder
3. sore
4. elbow
5. hurt (*or* ache)
6. has
7. aches (*or* hurts)
8. His
9. pain

D.

1. Does her stomach hurt?
2. Do their shoulders ache?
3. Is she sick?
4. Is the pain in his knee? (*or* Does he have a pain in his knee?)
5. Is your knee sore?
6. Does your wife have a stomachache?
7. Did he hurt his arm yesterday?
8. Do you feel better today?

Diálogo

1. b
2. b
3. b
4. a
5. a
6. a

Examen

1. hurts
2. earache
3. pain
4. ankle
5. feel
6. sharp
7. ache
8. matter
9. sore

Lección

2

Encontrará las respuestas en la página 24.

A. Elija la palabra correcta.

Ejemplo: He has a (runny)/running nose.

1. Please take your fever/temperature.

2. Is your throat sore/hurt?

3. She is cough/coughing.

4. The advice/symptom was very helpful.

5. The pharmacy/pharmacist will answer your question.

6. That was a loud sneezing/sneeze.

7. Is your left arm numbness/numb?

8. I have some congestion/dizziness in my chest.

9. In the US, people use Celsius/Fahrenheit thermometers.

10. You should go home and rest/go home.

B. Sopa de letras

Encuentre las palabras de la lista siguiente en el cuadro de abajo. Tenga en cuenta que las palabras se leen de izquierda a derecha y de arriba abajo.

advice, appointment, cold, cough, drugstore, fever, flu, ill, pharmacy, rest, runny nose, should, sneeze, sore, symptom, temperature, thermometer

T	E	M	P	E	R	A	T	U	R	E
H	H	A	H	S	M	P	F	L	U	U
E	T	R	A	Y	U	P	A	G	N	D
R	S	A	R	M	C	O	L	D	N	R
M	H	D	M	P	O	I	I	I	Y	U
O	O	V	A	T	A	N	F	L	N	G
M	U	I	C	O	H	T	E	L	O	S
E	L	C	Y	M	N	M	V	I	S	T
T	D	E	A	S	N	E	E	Z	E	O
E	C	O	U	G	H	N	R	G	Y	R
R	E	S	T	I	U	T	S	O	R	E

Encontrará las respuestas en la página 25.

C. Complete las oraciones con "should" o "shouldn't".

Ejemplo: She has a backache. She ___*shouldn't*___ lift that heavy box.

1. He has a cold. He _____ drink a lot of fluids.

2. His temperature is 98.6° He _____ worry.

3. You have a sharp pain in your chest. You _____ call the doctor now.

4. Those shoes hurt my feet. I _____ wear them.

5. She has a headache. She _____ take some aspirin.

6. They are too tired. They _____ work so hard.

7. He's a doctor. You _____ take his advice.

8. You _____ pick up that prescription today.

D. Conteste a las preguntas relacionadas con los dibujos.

Ejemplo: What's the matter?

Mark is sneezing.

Is he coughing?

No, he's sneezing.

1.   Is he coughing?

_____

2.   Does he have a cough?

_____

3. Is his nose running?

    _____

4. Does he have a runny nose?

    _____

5. Does he have an earache or a sore throat?

    _____

6. How does he feel?

    _____

7. Is he taking his temperature?

    _____

8. Does he have a fever?

    _____

② Diálogo

Encontrará las respuestas en la página 26.

Llene los espacios en blanco.

Ken   _____, Maribel and Anna. How are _____?

Maribel   I feel great.

Anna   _____, too. How are you,_____?

Ken   _____ too good.

Maribel   _____ the matter?

Ken   I have _____ cold.

Anna   Does _____ throat hurt?

Ken   _____ little. I cough all the time.

Maribel   Do you have a _____?

Ken   I _____ know. I didn't_____ my temperature. Achoo!

Maribel   Oh, _____ you.

Ken   Thanks. I _____ a pain in my chest, too.

Maribel   Is _____ a sharp pain?

Ken   No. My chest aches. _____ whole body aches!

            And I have _____ earache!

Anna   Do you have a stomachache, _____?

Ken   No.

Anna   Sorry, I'm just kidding. You should_____ home _____ rest.

Maribel   That _____ like a good idea.

Ken   _____ does sound like a good idea.

Encontrará las respuestas en la página 26.

John está hablando con la enfermera. Ponga las oraciones de esta conversación en el orden correcto.

_____ What are your symptoms?

_____ I don't feel well.

_____ OK, thank you very much. Goodbye.

_____ No, it doesn't.

_1_ This is the nurse. How can I help you?

_____ A little. My temperature is 99.9°.

_____ Drink lots of fluids, rest and take two aspirin. Call me tomorrow if you don't feel better.

_____ My head aches. I have a runny nose and my throat is sore.

_____ That's not too bad. Does it hurt when you breath?

_____ Do you have a fever?

Vocabulario

A.

1. temperature
2. sore
3. coughing
4. advice
5. pharmacist
6. sneeze
7. numb
8. congestion
9. Fahrenheit
10. rest

B.

T	E	M	P	E	R	A	T	U	R	E
H	H	A	H	S	M	P	F	L	U	U
E	T	R	A	Y	U	P	A	G	N	D
R	S	A	R	M	C	O	L	D	N	R
M	H	D	M	P	O	I	I	I	Y	U
O	O	V	A	T	A	N	F	L	N	G
M	U	I	C	O	H	T	E	L	O	S
E	L	C	Y	M	N	M	V	I	S	T
T	D	E	A	S	N	E	E	Z	E	O
E	C	O	U	G	H	N	R	G	Y	R
R	E	S	T	I	U	T	S	O	R	E

Clase

C.

1. should
2. shouldn't
3. should
4. shouldn't
5. should
6. shouldn't
7. should
8. should

D.

1. Yes, he is.
2. Yes, he does.
3. Yes, it is.
4. Yes, he does.
5. He has a sore throat.
6. He feels terrible.
7. Yes, he is.
8. Yes, he does./No, he doesn't./I don't know.

Diálogo

Ken	<u>Hi</u>, Maribel and Anna. How are <u>you</u>?
Maribel	I feel great.
Anna	<u>Me</u>, too. How are you, <u>Ken</u>?
Ken	<u>Not</u> too good.
Maribel	<u>What's</u> the matter?
Ken	I have <u>a</u> cold.
Anna	Does <u>your</u> throat hurt?
Ken	<u>A</u> little. I cough all the time.
Maribel	Do you have a <u>fever</u>?
Ken	I <u>don't</u> know. I didn't <u>take</u> my temperature. Achoo!
Maribel	Oh, <u>bless</u> you.
Ken	Thanks. I <u>have</u> a pain in my chest, too.
Maribel	Is <u>it</u> a sharp pain?
Ken	No. My chest aches. <u>My</u> whole body aches! And I have <u>an</u> earache!
Anna	Do you have a stomachache, <u>too</u>?
Ken	No.
Anna	Sorry, I'm just kidding. You should <u>go</u> home <u>and</u> rest.
Maribel	That <u>sounds</u> like a good idea.
Ken	<u>That</u> (*or* <u>It</u>) does sound like a good idea.

Examen

3 What are your symptoms?

2 I don't feel well.

10 OK, thank you very much. Goodbye.

8 No, it doesn't.

1 This is the nurse. How can I help you?

6 A little. My temperature is 99.9°.

9 Drink lots of fluids, rest and take two aspirin.
   Call me tomorrow if you don't feel better.

4 My head aches. I have a runny nose and my throat is sore.

7 That's not too bad. Does it hurt when you breath?

5 Do you have a fever?

Lección

3

3 Notas

Encontrará las respuestas en la página 35.

A. Relacione cada número, símbolo o expresión con una de las categorías siguientes.

key pad	telephone number	appointment time
medical insurance identification number		medical center address

Ejemplo: #   _____*key pad*_____

1. 0   _____

2. 555-1299   _____

3. 10:30, Tuesday   _____

4. 2298GG3   _____

5. 449 Oak Street   _____

6. (310) 555-3333   _____

7. *   _____

8. 895 Main   _____

9. 2:00 PM   _____

10. ID#342-88-12   _____

B. Ponga las letras en orden. Ya está colocada la primera letra.

1. eessnorp   r_____

2. eoaoprtr   o_____

3. gessmae   m _____

4. yombls   s_____

5. ntxameiaoni   e_____

6. toppmnetain   a_____

7. aaalebvil   a_____

8. preceisttnio   r_____

Encontrará las respuestas en la página 36.

C. Lea el correo electrónico que Gonzalo envió a su amiga Maritza y luego conteste a las preguntas.

Maritza, How are you doing? I was sick last week. I had the flu, I think. After two days, I called my doctor's office to make an appointment. It was about 7:00 PM. When I heard the voice on the phone, I started to talk. But the voice just kept talking, telling me to press different numbers. It was an answering machine!

I couldn't understand anything. I listened to the whole message and then I hung up the phone and went to bed. I stayed in bed for two more days.

I didn't go to the doctor but I feel better now. Next time I'll be ready for the answering machine. Best, Gonzalo

1. When was Gonzalo sick?

   _____

2. What was wrong with him?

   _____

3. What time did Gonzalo call the doctor?

   _____

4. Who answered the phone?

   _____

5. Did Gonzalo make an appointment?

   _____

6. How does Gonzalo feel now?

   _____

D. Lea la respuesta de Maritza. Haga un círculo alrededor de la palabra correcta.

Dear Gonzalo,

I'm glad you 1. (are/were) better now. Listening to the message on an

answering machine 2. (is/was) usually difficult. Sometimes you 3. (could/can)

listen to the message again. At the end of the message, the voice 4. (will/is)

give you directions. It will say something like, 5. "(Pressing/Press) 1 to listen

to the message again." Then you can listen to the message again and again—until

you 6. (understand/understood) it! This 7. (happened/happens) to me almost

every week. Take care and I 8. (will not/will) call you next week.

Your friend, Maritza

Encontrará las respuestas en la página 37.

Dibuje una línea que una la pregunta de la recepcionista con la respuesta correspondiente.

Receptionist	Patient
How can I help you?	It's 100.2°.
What are your symptoms?	Excuse me. Did you say 2:15 or 2:50?
What is your temperature?	It's 4670AK2.
Would you like to make an appointment?	I have a fever and a sore throat.
Can you come this afternoon at 2:50?	I don't feel well.
2:50. What is your insurance number?	Yes, please.

Encontrará las respuestas en la página 37.

Lea el mensaje grabado en el contestador automático. Luego, lea las oraciones y decida qué tecla se tiene que pulsar en cada caso.

Thank you for calling Dr. King's office. To hear this message in Spanish, press 2. To leave a message for the receptionist, press 3. To leave a message for the nurse, press 4. If you'd like to make or confirm an appointment, press 3. To schedule tests, please press 4. To leave a private message for Dr. King, press 5. If this is an emergency, dial 911. To hear this message again, press the star key.

Ejemplo: Juan doesn't speak English. ___*press 2*___

1. Maryanne wants to leave a message for the doctor. _____

2. Joe wants to confirm his appointment. _____

3. Elizabeth needs an X-ray. _____

4. Mr. Topp cut his finger very badly. _____

5. Julie didn't understand the message. _____

6. Mariah wants to leave a message for the nurse. _____

Vocabulario

A.

1. key pad
2. telephone number
3. appointment time
4. medical insurance identification number
5. medical center address
6. telephone number
7. key pad
8. medical center address
9. appointment time
10. medical insurance identification number

B.

1. response
2. operator
3. message
4. symbol
5. examination
6. appointment
7. available
8. receptionist

Clase

C.

1. He was sick last week.
2. He thinks he had the flu.
3. He called the doctor at about 7:00 PM.
4. An answering machine answered the phone.
5. No, Gonzalo didn't make an appointment.
6. He feels better.

D.

1. are
2. is
3. can
4. will
5. Press
6. understand
7. happens
8. will

Diálogo

Receptionist	Patient
How can I help you?	I don't feel well.
What are your symptoms?	I have a fever and a sore throat.
What is your temperature?	It's 100.2°.
Would you like to make an appointment?	Yes, please.
Can you come this afternoon at 2:50?	Excuse me. Did you say 2:15 or 2:50?
2:50. What is your insurance number?	It's 4670AK2.

Examen

1. press 5
2. press 3
3. press 4
4. dial 911
5. press the star key
6. press 4

Lección

4 Notas

Encontrará las respuestas en la página 47.

A. Sopa de letras

Encuentre las palabras de la lista siguiente en el cuadro de abajo. Tenga en cuenta que las palabras se leen de izquierda a derecha y de arriba abajo.

bottle, capsule, cause, dosage, empty, exactly, full, label, liquid, medication, once, pill, possible, powder, prescribe, refill, tablet, twice

M	E	D	I	C	A	T	I	O	N	F	P
P	X	O	N	C	E	A	H	O	E	U	A
R	A	S	L	A	C	B	O	T	T	L	E
E	C	A	I	U	E	L	E	W	E	L	M
S	T	G	Q	S	R	E	F	I	L	L	P
C	L	E	U	E	L	T	T	C	I	A	T
R	Y	P	I	L	L	D	F	E	L	B	Y
I	W	E	D	C	A	P	S	U	L	E	T
B	K	P	O	W	D	E	R	S	N	L	S
E	P	O	S	S	I	B	L	E	R	T	E

B. Haga un círculo alrededor de la palabra correcta.

Ejemplo: Be sure to (make/take) an appointment.

1. This medicine should/may cause drowsiness.

2. Did you take/give his temperature?

3. How many symptoms/refills does the prescription have?

4. Did the doctor give/take you a prescription?

5. The nurse asked/told me what my symptoms were.

6. Make sure you take/make the correct dose.

7. The label says to take one tablet each/once morning.

8. The possible/recommended dosage is one tablespoon daily.

Encontrará las respuestas en la página 48.

C. Relacione cada oración con su abreviatura correspondiente.

2 tsp. 3 X day	3 tabs. daily	1 tbsp. 2 X day
2 caps. 2 X day	1 tsp. w/ food	1 tsp. on empty stomach
1 cap. in AM	2 tabs. 2 X day	1 tbsp. as needed

Ejemplo: Take 2 teaspoons three times a day. ___*2 tsp, 3 X day*___

1. Take one tablespoon twice a day. _____

2. Take one capsule in the morning. _____

3. Take three tablets daily. _____

4. Take two tablets twice a day. _____

5. Take one teaspoon on an empty stomach. _____

6. Take two capsules twice a day. _____

7. Take one tablespoon as needed. _____

8. Take one teaspoon with food. _____

D. Ponga la letra correspondiente a cada instrucción en la columna correcta.

a. Do not mix with milk or milk products.

b. Caution: may cause drowsiness.

c. Take as needed.

d. Take with lots of water.

e. Take three tablespoons daily.

f. Take every evening.

g. Take all the pills.

h. Take in the morning.

i. No refills.

j. Do not exceed recommended dosage.

k. #1442900J

l. Take before bed.

When?	How much?	How?	Other
		a	

Encontrará las respuestas en la página 48.

Elija la oración que corresponde con las instrucciones.

1. Caution: May cause drowsiness.

   a) Don't take the medicine and drive.

   b) Take the medicine before you leave for work.

2. Take on an empty stomach.

   a) Don't take on a full stomach.

   b) Be sure to eat before you take the medicine.

3. Take before bed.

   a) Any time before noon is good.

   b) Take it just before you go to sleep.

4. Do not mix with other antibiotics.

   a) Do not take any aspirin.

   b) Tell your doctor if you are taking other antibiotics.

5. Do not take if you have a fever.

   a) Take your temperature first.

   b) If you have a fever, take this medicine.

6. Two tablespoons each morning for seven days.

   a) There are no refills for this prescription.

   b) You'll need a spoon to take the medicine.

Encontrará las respuestas en la página 49.

Lea la etiqueta. Luego, conteste a las preguntas.

Beverly Medical Pharmacy
8770 Beverly
LA, CA   310-555-9990
3422950
Dr. H. Wu

James Smith   8/24
Cozzard 100 MG Tab   #30
Take one tablet daily.
Take on an empty stomach.
Refills: 3

1.   Who is the patient?

_____

2.   What is the name of the doctor?

_____

3.   What is the prescription number?

_____

4.   What is the name of the pharmacy?

_____

5.   What is the name of the medicine?

_____

6.   What is the dosage?

_____

7.   Are there any cautions?

_____

8.   How many refills are there?

_____

Vocabulario

A.

M	E	D	I	C	A	T	I	O	N	F	P
P	X	O	N	C	E	A	H	O	E	U	A
R	A	S	L	A	C	B	O	T	T	L	E
E	C	A	I	U	E	L	E	W	E	L	M
S	T	G	Q	S	R	E	F	I	L	L	P
C	L	E	U	E	L	T	T	C	I	A	T
R	Y	P	I	L	L	D	F	E	L	B	Y
I	W	E	D	C	A	P	S	U	L	E	T
B	K	P	O	W	D	E	R	S	N	L	S
E	P	O	S	S	I	B	L	E	R	T	E

B.

1. may
2. take
3. refills
4. give
5. asked
6. take
7. each
8. recommended

Clase

C.

1. 1 tbsp. 2 X day
2. 1 cap. in AM
3. 3 tabs. daily
4. 2 tabs. 2 X day
5. 1 tsp. on empty stomach
6. 2 caps. 2 X day
7. 1 tbsp. as needed
8. 1 tsp. w/food

D.

When?   c, f, h, l

How much? e, g, j

How?   a, d,

Other   b, i, k

Diálogo

1. a)
2. a)
3. b)
4. b)
5. a)
6. b)

Examen

1. James Smith.
2. Dr. H. Wu.
3. # 3422950.
4. Beverly Medical Pharmacy.
5. Cozzard.
6. One tablet daily. *or* 100 MG daily.
7. Yes. Take on an empty stomach.
8. Three.

Aprendamos Viajando

Notas

Boston

Antes de completar este ejercicio, vea la sección "Aprendamos viajando" incluida en el video y lea la misma sección en el manual.

Si la información contenida en la oración es verdadera, haga un círculo alrededor de la palabra **True**. Si la información es falsa, haga un círculo alrededor de la palabra **False** y escriba una oración con la información correcta.

True *False*   1. Boston is in Massachusetts.

_____

True *False*   2. Many events related to the Revolutionary War took place in Boston.

_____

True *False*   3. It is called "Europe's American City."

_____

True *False*   4. The Freedom Train is a tour of historic sites.

_____

True *False*   5. Paul Revere began his midnight ride at the Old North Church.

_____

True   *False*   6. The Boston Coffee Party was a famous event.

_____

True   *False*   7. Faneuil Hall is called the "Cradle of Liberty."

_____

True   *False*   8. Italian is spoken on the streets of the North End.

_____

True   *False*   9. The New England Aquarium is on East Wharf.

_____

True   *False*   10. Harvard and MIT are in Cambridge.

_____

True   *False*   11. Harvard is called an Ivy Tree school.

_____

True   *False*   12. MIT is known for its scientific research.

_____

1. True.
2. True.
3. False. It is called "America's European City."
4. False. The Freedom Trail is a tour of historic sites.
5. True.
6. False. The Boston Tea Party was a famous event.
7. True.
8. True.
9. False. It's on Central Wharf.
10. True.
11. False. Harvard is an Ivy League school.
12. True.

Notas

Para información sobre
Inglés sin Barreras
en oferta especial de
Referido Preferido
1-800-305-6472
Dé el Código 03429

Examen Final 8

Llene el círculo correspondiente a la respuesta correcta.

1. *My shoulder _____.*
   - O a) has a backache
   - O b) is a pain
   - O c) pains
   - O d) aches
   - O e) ache

2. *_____ his elbow _____?*
   - O a) Why does, hurts
   - O b) Why, aches
   - O c) Do, aches
   - O d) Do, ache
   - O e) Does, hurt

3. *Do you _____ earache?*
   - O a) hurt some
   - O b) have an
   - O c) have
   - O d) have a
   - O e) hurt an

4. *What's the _____?*
   - O a) stomache
   - O b) hurt
   - O c) hurt
   - O d) matter
   - O e) wrong

5. *I have a __ throat and a ____.*
   - O a) hurt, temperature
   - O b) ache, temperature
   - O c) sore, fever
   - O d) sore, runny
   - O e) fever, sore

6. *The pharmacist's _____ was very helpful.*
   - O a) temperature
   - O b) cold
   - O c) prescribe
   - O d) symptom
   - O e) advice

7. *Those shoes hurt my feet. _____ wear them.*
   - O a) I shouldn't
   - O b) She should
   - O c) I can
   - O d) She can
   - O e) I am

8. *You are _____ a lot. You should see the doctor.*
   - O a) ache
   - O b) fever
   - O c) coughing
   - O d) runny nose
   - O e) sneeze

9. *Drink lots of ___ rest and take two _____.*
   - O a) orange juice, pill
   - O b) coffee, medicines
   - O c) fluids, aspirin
   - O d) medicine, tablets
   - O e) water, capsule

10. *Listening to the message on an answering machine _____ usually difficult.*
    - O a) happened
    - O b) is
    - O c) shouldn't
    - O d) has
    - O e) happens

11. *To hear this _____ again, press the star key.*
    - O a) appointments
    - O b) reception
    - O c) speaking
    - O d) phone
    - O e) message

12. *This medicine __ cause drowsiness.*
    - O a) don't
    - O b) should
    - O c) wasn't
    - O d) isn't
    - O e) may

13. *___does the prescription have?*
    - O a) When
    - O b) How much
    - O c) How many refills
    - O d) How many
    - O e) How possible

14. *Did the doctor __ you a prescription?*
    - O a) give
    - O b) mark
    - O c) make
    - O d) recommended
    - O e) tell

15. *2 tsp. 3 X day _____*
    - O a) Take three tablets daily.
    - O b) Take 2 teaspoons at 3:00 each day.
    - O c) Take two tablets twice a day.
    - O d) Take 2 tablespoons three times a day.
    - O e) Take 2 teaspoons three times a day.

Cuando termine el examen, córtelo en la línea de puntos y envíelo a:

Inglés sin Barreras
Post Office Box 75175
Los Angeles, California 90075-0175
U.S.A.

Fecha _____

N.° de contrato _____

Teléfono (_____) _____

Si lo prefiere, puede enviarlo por fax al (323) 782-7466. Responderemos por fax.

Fax (_____) _____

www.inglessinbarreras.com

Por favor, escriba claramente su nombre y dirección (use tinta oscura) para que podamos enviarle el examen corregido.

Nombre _____

Dirección _____

Ciudad _____ Estado _____

Código Postal _____ País _____